Joyride

By Arielle Haughee

Illustrated by Fay Becca

ORANGE BLOSSOM
PUBLISHING

To Dizey, Sneeda, and Mr. Floorsnacks —A.H.

To my wonderful husband for his patience, understanding and unceasing support and to my sweet puppy Daisy for her crazy antics which continually inspires me, as an artist, to see the world from her point of view. —FayBecca

Published 2019 by Orange Blossom Publishing
Maitland, Florida
info@orangeblossombooks.com
www.orangeblossombooks.com

Cover Layout, Typesetting, and Interior Formatting: Battle Goddess Productions
Watercolor Illustration: Becky McKinness
Art Photography: The Inspired Storytellers

Paperback Edition ISBN: 978-1-949935-08-0
Hardback Edition ISBN: 978-1-949935-09-7
Digital Edition ISBN: 978-1-949935-10-3

LCCN: 2019915565

Printed in the USA

Leo perched on his sill, the best place to be.
He had sun, he had calm, and all he could see.

When along came Daisy, all ready to play.
She whined and she whimpered in that puppy dog way.

"Come down here, Leo, I know what to do.
We'll have an adventure, just me and you."

Daisy opened the door.
A bike stood outside.
Her eyes glittered bright.

"Let's go for a ride!"

Leo shook his head no. His happy was here,
but a cricket hopped up and looked ready to steer.

His whiskers, they twitched. He must get it NOW.
Leo leaped out the door with a hearty **ME-OW!**

Daisy hopped on the bike and made the bell ring. "We'll **ZOOM** to the park and ride on the swing!"

The wind, how it whipped! Poor Leo clung tight.

This was **terrible, awful**—

he'd have nightmares tonight.

The cricket just chirped and Daisy yelled,

"Weeeee!"

Then they flew down the hill and crashed into a tree.

8

Leo yelped and he yowled, "I want to go home!
No more adventures.

Just leave me alone!"

"Now, Leo," she said, as a golf cart stopped near. "Our fun isn't over. We have to ride here!"

"What are you, crazy?" It was time to say no, but that cricket hopped in and was ready to go.

Just one solid pounce—he'd finish his quest.
Leo needed to, HAD to show he was the best.

The golf cart took off. Daisy knew how to drive!
She **zipped** and she **zooped**—and she felt so alive.

Not Leo. No. No.
He clawed at the seat,
screeching and **sliding**
and kicking his feet.

13

They drove through the park then down by the shore.
The sand made it harder to drive than before.

The tires, they spun making **arches** of grit.
This ride was over. Time for Leo to split.

He leapt to the beach and Daisy jumped down.
She yipped and she yapped but Leo just frowned.

He licked off some sand. "You think this is fun? This madness? This chaos? I tell you— **I'M DONE."**

It was time to go back to where it was warm, his window, his sill, his calm from the storm.

Then there it was, that ridiculous cricket.
He bounced on the shore and into the thicket.

Leo crouched down low, his eyes opened wide,
    and just as he leapt, it hopped into the tide.

19

Leo couldn't give up. This was no time to fail.
As he sprang right behind, his claws sunk in a...sail?

A boat? Yes, a boat. Now this was all wrong.
Leo hated the water and didn't belong.

Daisy bounded aboard. "Now there is the spirit!"

Leo dropped to the deck, too frightened to hear it.

Then the boat made a turn and around came the boom.

Poor Leo went flying.

ZUH-ZUH-ZUH-ZOOOOOOOOOM!

OH NO!

He splashed in the water, refusing to swim.
It was cold, it was drippy. How'd this happen to him?

Leo angrily sank to the sandy sea floor.

His happy was gone.

Could there be any more?

He reached out his paws then kicked with his feet.
He **glided**. He **swirled**. This couldn't be beat!

"Daisy, my buddy, jump in! Let's all play!
It's better than sitting at home for the day."

This was different and fun. A new way to be—
out in the world, with friends being free.

They all swam together under the sun.
Daisy smiled and said, "Our joyride is done.
Let's go home, Leo. I like it there, too."

Leo gave her a wink, "The joy is with you."

The End

Lightning Source UK Ltd.
Milton Keynes UK
UKRC011510291119
354466UK00001B/3